CONTENTS

THE POSSUM TREE
161 poems for children

Selected by
Lesley Pyott

A & C Black ● London

Published by A & C Black (Publishers) Limited
35 Bedford Row, London WC1R 4JH

First published in 1983, as *The Best Primary Poetry Anthology —
Ever!*, by Longman Cheshire Pty Ltd, Longman Cheshire House,
Kings Gardens, 91-97 Coventry Street, Melbourne 3205,
Australia.
This edition first published in 1985 by A & C Black (Publishers)
Limited.

ISBN 0 7136 2706 9

Designed by Stanley Wong
Illustrated by Andrew and Julian Wong
Cover illustration by Satoshi Kitamura

The Possum Tree   161 poems for children
1. English poetry
I. Pyott, Lesley   II. The Possum Tree: best primary poetry
anthology ever.
821'.008'09282 PR1175

ISBN 0-7136-2706-9

COLONEL FAZACKERLEY

Colonel Fazackerley Butterworth-Toast
Bought an old castle complete with a ghost,
But someone or other forgot to declare
To Colonel Fazack that the spectre was there.

On the very first evening, while waiting to dine,
The Colonel was taking a fine sherry wine,
When the ghost, with a furious flash and a flare,
Shot out of the chimney and shivered, "Beware!"

Colonel Fazackerley put down his glass
And said, "My dear fellow, that's really first class!
I just can't conceive how you do it at all.
I imagine you're going to a Fancy Dress Ball?"

At this, the dread ghost gave a withering cry,
Said the Colonel (his monocle firm in his eye),
"Now just how you do it I wish I could think.
Do sit down and tell me, and please have a drink.

The ghost in his phosphorous cloak gave a roar
And floated about between ceiling and floor.
He walked through a wall and returned through a pane
And backed up the chimney and came down again.

Said the Colonel, "With laughter I'm feeling quite weak!"
(As trickles of merriment ran down his cheek).
"My house warming party I hope you won't spurn.
You must say you'll come and you'll give us a turn".

At this, the poor spectre — quite out of his wits —
Proceeded to shake himself almost to bits.
He rattled his chains and he clattered his bones
And he filled the whole castle with mumbles and moans.

But Colonel Fazackerley just as before,
Was simply delighted and called out, "Encore!"
At which the ghost vanished, his efforts in vain,
And never was seen at the castle again.

"Oh dear, what a pity" said Colonel Fazack.
"I don't know his name, so I can't call him back".
And then with a smile that was hard to define,
Colonel Fazackerley went in to dine.

Charles Causley

THE OLD WIFE AND THE GHOST

There was an old wife and she lived all alone
In a cottage not far from Hitchin;
And one bright night, by the full moonlight,
Comes a ghost right into her kitchen.

About that kitchen neat and clean
The ghost goes pottering round.
But the poor old wife is deaf as a boot
And so heard never a sound.

The ghost blows up the kitchen fire,
As bold as bold can be;
He helps himself from the larder shelf,
But never a sound hears she.

He blows on his hands to make them warm,
And whistles aloud "Whee-hee!"
But still as a sack the old soul lies
And never a sound hears she.

From corner to corner he runs about,
And into the cupboard he peeps;
He rattles the door and bumps on the floor,
But still the old wife sleeps.

Jangle and bang go the pots and pans,
As he throws them all around;
And the plates and mugs and dishes and jugs,
He flings them all to the ground.

Madly the ghost tears up and down
And screams like a storm at sea;
And at last the old wife stirs in her bed —
And it's "Drat those mice", says she.

Then the first cock crows and morning shows
And the troublesome ghost's away.
But oh! what a pickle the poor wife sees
When she gets up next day.

"Them's tidy big mice," the old wife thinks,
And off she goes to Hitchin;
And a tidy big cat she fetches back
To keep the mice from her kitchen.

James Reeves

3

QUEER THINGS

'Very, very queer things have been happening to me
In some of the places where I've been.
I went to the pillar-box this morning with a letter
And a hand came out and took it in.

'When I got home again, I thought I'd have
A glass of spirits to steady myself;
And I take my bible oath, but that bottle and glass
Came a-hopping down off the shelf.

'No, no, I says, I'd better take no spirits,
And I sat down to have a cup of tea;
And blowed if my old pair of carpet-slippers
Didn't walk across the carpet to me!

'So I took my newspaper and went into the park,
And looked round to see no one was near,
When a voice right out of the middle of the paper
Started reading the news bold and clear!

'Well, I guess there's some magician out to help me,
So perhaps there's no need for alarm;
And if I manage not to anger him,
Why should he do me any harm?'

James Reeves

Questions

1.   *What would you do if you saw a ghost?*

2.   *How did Colonel Fazackerley get rid of the ghost?*

3.   *In the last verse, why was Colonel Fazackerley smiling?*

4.   *How do the ghosts in "Colonel Fazackerley" and
     "The Old Wife and the Ghost" behave in the same way?
     Are they successful? Why not?*

HALLOWE'EN

This is the night
When witches fly,
On their broomsticks,
Through the sky.

Each one has
A small black cat,
And each one wears
A pointed hat.

Into their cauldrons
They toss in all
The frogs and snails
And lizards small.

Mice and spiders
They use as well,
As each one weaves
A magic spell.

With tongue of bee,
And hiss of snake,
In coal-black cauldrons,
Spells they make.

Bats' wings flutter,
Owls fly high,
When witches prowl
Across the sky.

A. Ruddich

THE HAG

The Hag is astride,
   This night for to ride;
The Devil and she together:
   Through thick, and through thin,
   Now out, and then in,
Though ne'er so foul be the weather.

   A Thorn or a Burr
   She takes for a Spur:
With a lash of a Bramble she rides now,
   Through brakes and through briars,
   O'er Ditches and Mires,
She follows the Spirit that guides now.

   No Beast, for his food,
   Dares now range the wood;
But hush'd in his lair he lies lurking:
   While mischiefs, by these,
   On land and on Seas,
At noon of Night are a working.

   The storm will arise,
   And trouble the skies;
This night, and more for the wonder,
   The ghost from the Tomb
   Affrighted shall come,
Called out by the clap of the Thunder.

Robert Herrick

HALLOWE'EN

Ruggledy-Guggledy, goblins and ghouls,
Witches bring your witches' tools.
Broomsticks, cauldrons and jet black cats,
Put on your cloaks and high pointed hats.

Raggledy-Gaggledy, Hallowe'en's here,
Magic and Spells, when night-time is near.
Witches on broomsticks fly in the sky,
Screaming and squealing when the moon's riding high.

Riggledy-Giggledy, witches beware,
It's getting light, so you must take care.
You'll have to go before morning's light —
Because witches only come out at night.

Mollie I. Leeds

THE RIDE–BY–NIGHTS

Up on their brooms the witches stream,
Crooked and black in the crescent's gleam;
One foot high and one foot low,
Bearded, cloaked, and cowled, they go.
'Neath Charlie's Wain they twitter and tweet
And away they swarm 'neath the Dragon's feet,
With a whoop and a flutter they swing and sway,
And surge pell-mell down the Milky Way.
Between the legs of the glittering Chair
They hover and squeak in the empty air.
Then round they swoop past the glimmering Lion
To where Sirius barks behind huge Orion;
Up, then, and over to wheel amain
Under the silver, and home again.

Walter de la Mare

SPACE TRAVELLERS

There was a witch, hump-backed and hooded.
   Lived by herself in a burnt-out tree.
Where storm winds shrieked and the moon was buried
   And the dark of the forest was black as black.
   She rose in the air like a rocket at sea.
      Riding the wind,
      Riding the night,
   Riding the tempest to the moon and back.

There may be a man with a hump of silver
   Telescope eyes and a telephone ear,
Dials to twist and knobs to twiddle,
   Waiting for a night when skies are clear,
   To shoot from the scaffold with a blazing track,
      Riding the dark,
      Riding the cold,
   Riding the silence to the moon and back.

James Nimmo

MOTHS AND MOONSHINE

Moths and moonshine mean to me
Magic — madness — mystery.

Witches dancing weird and wild
Mischief make for man and child,

Owls screech from woodland shades,
Moths glide through moonlit glades,

Moving in dark and secret wise
Like a plotter in disguise.

Moths and moonshine mean to me
Magic — madness — mystery.

James Reeves

THE WITCHES' CALL

Come, witches, come, on your hithering brooms!
The moorland is dark and still —
Over the church and the churchyard tombs
To the oakwood under the hill.
Come through the mist and wandering cloud,
Fly with the crescent moon;
Come where the witches and warlocks crowd,
Come away . . . soon!

Leave your room with its shadowy cat,
Your cauldron over the hearth;
Seize your cloak and pointed hat,
Come by the witches' path.
Float from the earth like a rising bird,
Stream through the darkening air,
Come at the sound of our secret word,
Come to the witches' lair.

Clive Sansom

Things to do

1. Write your own poem about a witch, describing her
    looks, clothes, animals, broomstick and spells. Draw a
    picture of your witch.

2. Write a witch's spell. Think of all the things she might put
    into her cauldron, what she would chant and what the
    spell is for.

3. Write a poem about Hallowe'en when all the witches ride
    out and gather together.

CIRCUS PARADE

Here it comes! Here it comes!
I can hear the music playing;
I can hear the beating drums.

On parade! On parade!
Gaily plumed a horse and rider
Lead the circus cavalcade.

Knights in armour with their banners
Calmly riding by;
Horses hung with velvet trappings,
Stepping proudly high;
Circus wagons slowly clanking,
Drawn by six horse teams,
Red and gold and set with mirrors
Where the sunlight gleams;
Yawning lions in their cages;
Polar bear with swinging head;
Restless tiger pacing pacing
Back and forth with noiseless tread:
Horses snorting and cavorting
With wild yellow cowboy bands;
Dressed-up monkeys riding ponies,
Bowing as we clap our hands;
Herds of elephants and camels,
Marching one by one;
Troops of painted clowns advancing,
Playing tricks, and making fun.

At the end the steam calliope
Comes playing all too soon,
Saying the parade is over
As it pipes its wildest tune.

James S. Tippett

PARADE

This is the day the circus comes
With blare of brass, with beating drums,
And clashing cymbals, and with roar
Of wild beasts never heard before
Within town limits. Spick and span
Will shine each gilded cage and van;
Cockades at every horse's head
Will nod, and riders dressed in red
Or blue trot by. There will be floats
In shapes like dragons, thrones and boats,
And clowns on stilts; freaks big and small,
Till leisurely and last of all
Camels and elephants will pass
Beneath our elms, along our grass.

Rachel Field

THE CIRCUS

Hey, there! Hoop-la! the circus is in town!
Have you seen the elephant? Have you seen the clown?
Have you seen the dappled horse gallop round the ring?
Have you seen the acrobats on the dizzy swing?
Have you seen the tumbling men tumble up and down?
Hoop-la! Hoop-la! the circus is in town!

Hey, there! Hoop-la! Here's the circus troupe!
Here's the educated dog jumping through the hoop.
See the lady Blondin with the parasol and fan,
The lad upon the ladder and the india-rubber man.
See the joyful juggler and the boy who loops the loop.
Hey! Hey! Hey! Hey! Here's the circus troupe!

C.J. Dennis

CIRCUS

The brass band blares,
The naphtha flares,
The sawdust smells,
Showmen ring bells,
And oh! right into the circus-ring
Comes such a lovely, lovely thing,
A milk-white pony with flying tress,
And a beautiful lady,
A beautiful lady,
A beautiful lady in a pink dress!
The red-and-white clown
For joy tumbles down,
Like a pink rose
Round she goes
On her tip-toes
With the pony under —
And then, oh, wonder!
The pony his milk-white tresses droops,
And the beautiful lady,
The beautiful lady,
Flies like a bird through the paper hoops!
The red-and-white clown for joy falls dead.
Then he waggles his feet and stands on his head,
And the little boys on the twopenny seats
Scream with laughter and suck their sweets.

Eleanor Farjeon

AT THE CIRCUS

The Elephants

With their trunks the elephants
Hold hands in a long row —
Their little eyes so quick and wise,
Their feet so big and slow.
They climb on top of things and then,
When they are told, climb down again.

Bare-back Rider

There isn't a prettier sight, I think,
Than a pony that's white and a lady that's pink:
The pony so frisky and stepping so high,
The lady so smiling as they go by,
The lady so tip-toe on her toes,
The pony, his bridle dressed up with a rose,
The lady and pony both liking to be
Riding around for the world to see.

The Seals

The seals all flap,
Their shining flips
And bounce balls on
Their nosey tips,
And beat a drum,
And catch a bar,
And wriggle with
How pleased they are.

Dorothy Aldis

EQUESTRIENNE

See, they are clearing the sawdust course
For the girl in pink on the milk white horse.
Her spangles twinkle; his pale flanks shine,
Every hair of his tail is fine
And bright as a comet's, his mane blows free,
And she points a toe and bends a knee,
And the while his hoofbeats fall like rain
Over and over and over again.
And nothing that moves on land or sea
Will seem so beautiful to me
As the girl in pink on the milk-white horse
Cantering over the sawdust course.

Rachel Field

AT THE CIRCUS

Last night the circus came to town,
And there I saw the most wonderful clown!
Oh, I saw other things as well —
A horse that danced and rang a bell,
A tiger that jumped through a burning ring,
A dog that counted and rode on a swing;
I saw elephants, lions, and bears, and seals,
And little dogs riding on big turning wheels,
And monkeys that played with a shining red ball —
But the clown was the very best thing of all!
He wore a suit of pink and black,
And hopped around with his feet in a sack;
He told funny stories and did magic tricks
With pigeons and candles and rabbits and sticks;
He juggled with balls, he sat on eight chairs
That stood on each other, piled high, in pairs;
He blew me a kiss when he waved goodbye,
And nobody clapped as loudly as I!
Oh, when can I go back to town
To see that wonderful circus clown?

Eva May

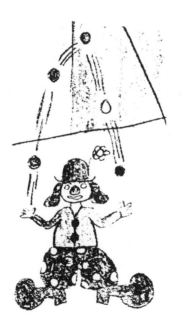

EPILOGUE

Nothing now to mark the spot
But a littered vacant lot;
Sawdust in a heap, and there
Where the ring was, grass worn bare.
In a circle, scuffed and brown,
And a paper hoop the clown
Made his little dog jump through,
And a pygmy pony-shoe.

Rachel Field

Things to do

1. *Write a poem about going to the circus. Think of one or
    two of the acts and describe them. Think of the
    atmosphere, noise and smells of the circus and try to
    describe them in your poem.*

HOT DOGS - 85c
DRINKS - 80c
ICY- POLES - 30c

MERRY-CO

TICKETS

ROUNDABOUT

The roundabout horses are back at the Show
    With a rig-a-jig-jig and away.
The music's begun, and they're rearing to go,
And the children are mounted, with faces a-glow,
    With a rig-a-jig-jig and away.

I'm up on a charger that's dappledy-grey,
    With a rig-a-jig-jig and away.
His saddle and harness are handsome and gay,
And I'm hoping he'll gallop and gallop all day,
    With a rig-a-jig-jig and away.

I'll play I'm a robber, the chief of the band,
    With a rig-a-jig-jig and away.
Or I'm off to Crusades, with a lance in my hand,
To harry the Saracens out of the land,
    With a rig-a-jig-jig and away.

And now I'm a farmer that's mustering stock,
    With a rig-a-jig-jig and away.
My sheep-dogs are helping to round up the flock,
While I ride in my saddle as firm as a rock,
    With a rig-a-jig-jig and away.

Or I'm just on a roundabout, back at the Show,
    With a rig-a-jig-jig and away.
For the music is blaring, we're ready to go,
And whether they're racing, or whether they're slow,
There isn't a joy you can possibly know
Like riding a roundabout horse at the Show,
    With a rig-a-jig-jig,
    And a rig-a-jig-jig,
    And a rig-a-jig-jig and away.

Lydia Pender

FUN FAIR

Riding high then riding low,
On our merry way we go,
Music blaring — lights ablaze,
Happy, happy, fun filled days.
Candy floss and lemonade,
Phew! Let's find a little shade.
Hoopla — darts to test your eye,
Shall we have another try.
Pocket money almost spent,
Goodness knows just where it went;
Having too much fun to care,
How we love it at the fair!

Philip F. Williams

FAIRGROUND

Organ-shout music, kaleidoscope streamers,
Big-Dipper hooters and Dodgem-'Em Car screamers,
Roundabout motors and buses and steamers,
'Walk up, folks . . .
'Walk up, folks, come to the . . . .'

Ear-splitting shooting range, trot-trotting donkeys,
Blue and red cockatoos, clambering monkeys,
Crowd noises, loud noises, shrill honky-tonkies,
'Walk up, folks . . .
'Walk up, folks, come to the . . . .'

Gipsy magicians, and goldfish for prizes,
Candy-floss sugar in gigantic sizes,
Heart stopping Ghost Train with screeching surprises,
'Walk up folks . . .
'Walk up, folks, come to the Fair. Come to the Fair!''

Marian Lines

THE ROUNDABOUT BY THE SEA

The crimson-spotted horses,
Long-tailed and glassy-eyed,
With feet outstretched before them
Go circling side by side;
Rising,
Falling,
In slow unthinking play —
All day.

On hoofs for ever silent
They climb or dip the air;
Some with their clinging riders,
Some riderless and bare;
Rising,
Falling,
With flash of bridles gay —
All day.

The old man turns his handle:
The horses creak and glide.
No other sound, no music
But the music of the tide.
Rising,
Falling,
In pebbled wash and spray —
All day.
All day.

John Walsh

Things to Do

*Write a poem about going to the show. Think of the
excitement, the smells of the food, the screams and noise of
the rides, the jostling of the crowds, the shouts of the
showmen and what it feels like on the rides. Try to convey the
atmosphere of the show in your poem.*

FROM A RAILWAY CARRIAGE

Faster than fairies, faster than witches,
Bridges and houses, hedges and ditches;
And charging along like troops in a battle,
All through the meadows the horses and cattle;
All of the sights of the hill and the plain
Fly as thick as driving rain:
And ever again, in the wink of an eye,
Painted stations whistle by.

Here is a child who clambers and scrambles,
All by himself and gathering brambles;
Here is a tramp who stands and gazes;
And there is the green for stringing the daisies!
Here is a cart run away in the road
Lumping along with man and load;
And here is a mill, and there is a river
Each a glimpse and gone for ever!

Robert Louis Stevenson

TRAINS

From my bedroom window
   I watch the trains go by,
On frosty winter evenings
   Beneath a starry sky.

Snorting, puffing, roaring,
   With windows all alight,
The trains, like fiery dragons,
   Go racing through the night.

Eileen B. Edge

THE TRAIN

Over the bridges and under the tunnels,
Faster and Faster I go.
Here is a station and waiting people,
Slower, slow, slow.
Slam! Slam! Slam!
The doors are closing,
Sh! Sh! Sh!
Off we go.

Margaret Wild

THE TRAIN

A green eye — and a red — in the dark,
Thunder — smoke — and a spark.

It is there — it is here — flashed by.
Whither will the wild thing fly?

It is rushing, tearing through the night.
Rending her gloom in its flight.

It shatters her silence with shrieks.
What is it the wild thing seeks?

Alas! for it hurries away
Them that are fain to stay.

Hurrah! for it carries home
Lovers and friends that roam.

Mary E. Coleridge

THE ENGINE DRIVER

The train goes running along the line,
   Jicketty — can, jicketty — can.
I wish it were mine, I wish it were mine,
   Jicketty — can, jicketty — can.
The Engine Driver stands in front —
   He makes it run, he makes it shunt.

      Out of the town,
      Out of the town,
      Over the hill,
      Over the down,
      Under the bridges,
      Across the lea,
      Over the ridges
      And down to the sea.

With a jicketty — can, jicketty — can,
Jicketty — jicketty — jicketty — can,
Jicketty — can, jicketty — can . . . .

                              Clive Sansom

TRAINS AT NIGHT

I like the whistle of trains at night,
The fast trains thundering by so proud!
They rush and rumble across the world,
They ring wild bells and they toot so loud!

But I love better the slower trains.
They take their time through the world instead,
And whistle softly and stop to tuck
Each sleepy blinking town in bed!

                              Frances M. Frost

Things to do

*Write a poem about a train journey. Try to get the rhythm and
noise of the train into your poem. Write about the sensation
of being on the train and about the things you see from the
window.*

TAKING OFF

The airplane taxis down the field
And heads into the breeze,
It lifts its wheels above the ground,
It skims above the trees,
It rises high and higher
Away up toward the sun,
It's just a speck against the sky
— And now it's gone!

Anon.

UP IN THE AIR

Zooming across the sky
Like a great bird you fly,
    Airplane,
    Silvery white
    In the light.

Turning and twisting in air,
When shall I ever be there,
    Airplane,
    Piloting you
    Far in the blue?

James S. Tippett

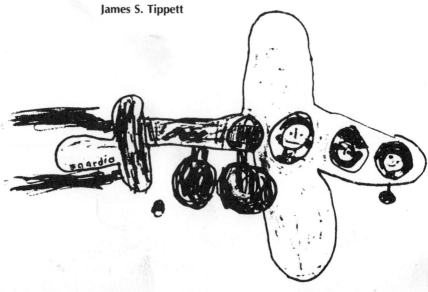

COCKPIT IN THE CLOUDS

Two thousand feet beneath our wheels
The city sprawls across the land
Like heaps of children's blocks outflung,
In tantrums, by a giant hand.
To east a silver spire soars
And seeks to pierce our lower wing.
Above its grasp we drift along,
A tiny, droning; shiny thing.

The noon crowds pack the narrow streets.
The el trains move so slow, so slow.
Amidst their traffic, chaos, life,
The city's busy millions go.
Up here, aloof, we watch them crawl.
In crystal air we seem to poise
Behind our motor's throaty roar —
Down there, we're just another noise.

Dick Dorrance

NIGHT PLANE

The midnight plane with its riding lights
looks like a footloose star
wandering west through the blue-black night
to where the mountains are,

a star that's journeyed nearer earth
to tell each quiet farm
and little town, "Put out your lights,
children of earth. Sleep warm."

Frances M. Frost

Things to do

*Write a poem about an aeroplane. Write about what it looks
like in the sky, the colour, shape and sound. If you have been
to an airport, write about the aeroplanes taking off and
landing. If you have been on an aeroplane journey write
about what it feels like to be in an aeroplane, the sensation of
taking off and landing, the noise and the view from the
window.*

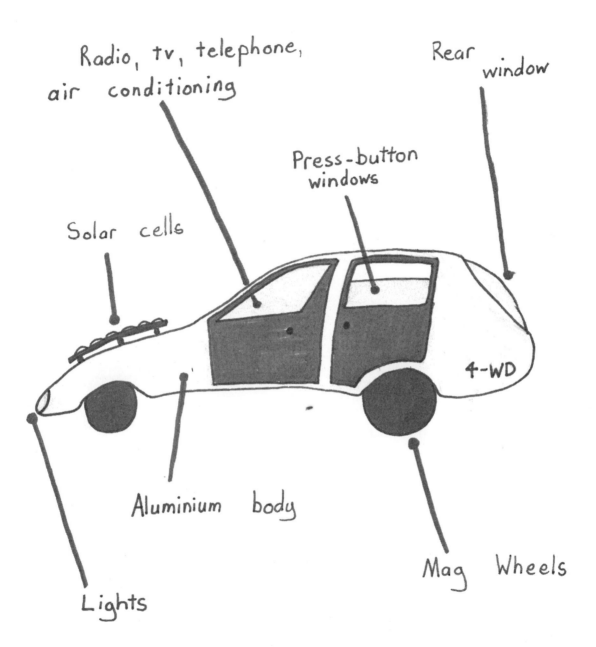

Radio, tv, telephone, air conditioning

Rear window

Solar cells

Press-button windows

4-WD

Aluminium body

Lights

Mag Wheels

MOTOR CARS

From city window, 'way up high,
I like to watch the cars go by.
They look like burnished beetles, black,
That leave a little muddy track
Behind them as they slowly crawl.
Sometimes they do not move at all
But huddle close with hum and drone
As though they feared to be alone.
They grope their way through fog and night
With the golden feelers of their light.

Rowena Bastin Bennett

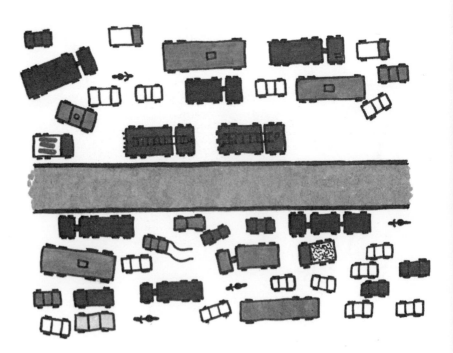

AUTOMOBILE MECHANICS

Sometimes
I help my dad
Work on our automobile.
We unscrew
The radiator cap
And we let some water run —
Swish — from a hose
Into the tank.

And then we open up the hood
And feed in oil
From a can with a long spout.
And then we take a lot of rags
And clean all about.
We clean the top
And the doors
And the fenders and the wheels
And the windows and floors . . .
We work hard
My dad
And I.

Dorothy Baruch

CARBREAKERS

There's a graveyard in our street,
But it's not for putting people in;
The bodies that they bury here
Are made of steel and paint and tin.

The people come and leave their wrecks
For crunching in the giant jaws
Of a great hungry car-machine,
That lives on bonnets, wheels and doors.

When I pass by the yard at night,
I sometimes think I hear a sound
Of ghostly horns that moan and whine,
Upon that metal-graveyard mound.

Marion Lines

CITY BEASTS

If I were in a jungle dark,
    I wouldn't cross a place
Where I might run into a lion
    Or tiger, face to face.

So in the city I will try
    To do the very same,
For everybody knows that cars
    Are not exactly tame!

I'll wait at corners when I should,
    Watch where I go, and see
That I'm not crossing any trails
    Where city beasts might be.

Frances Gorman Risser

Questions

The four poems show different aspects of cars.
Which poem do you like best and why?

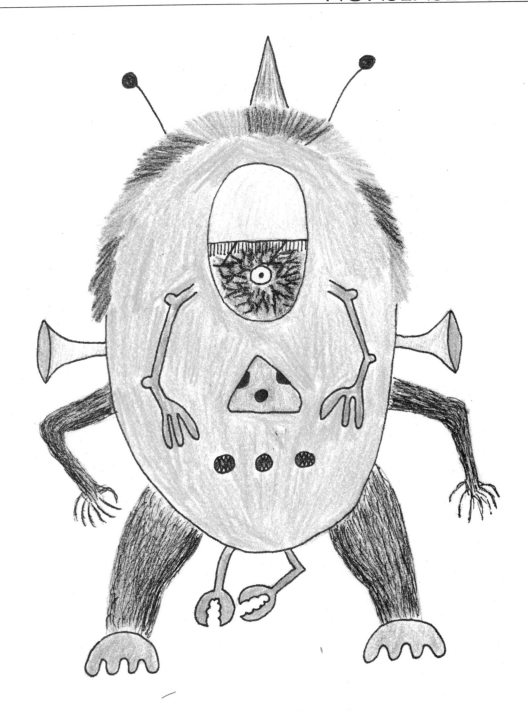

THE OWL AND THE PUSSY CAT

The Owl and the Pussy-Cat went to sea
In a beautiful pea-green boat,
They took some honey, and plenty of money,
Wrapped up in a five-pound note.
The Owl looked up to the stars above,
And sang to a small guitar,
"O lovely Pussy! O Pussy, my love,
What a beautiful Pussy you are,
    You are
    You are!
What a beautiful Pussy you are!"

Pussy said to the Owl, "You elegant fowl!
How charmingly sweet you sing!
O let us be married! too long we have tarried:
But what shall we do for a ring?"
They sailed away, for a year and a day,
To the land where the Bong-tree grows
And there in a wood a Piggy-wig stood
With a ring at the end of his nose,
    His nose,
    His nose,
With a ring at the end of his nose.

"Dear Pig, are you willing to sell for one shilling
Your ring?" Said the Piggy, "I will".
So they took it away, and were married next day
By the Turkey who lives on the hill.
They dined on mince, and slices of quince,
Which they ate with a runcible spoon;
And hand in hand, on the edge of the sand,
They danced by the light of the moon,
    The moon
    The moon,
They danced by the light of the moon.

Edward Lear

THE POBBLE WHO HAS NO TOES

The Pobble who has no toes
Had once as many as we;
When they said, "Some day you may lose them all;" —
He replied, — "Fish fiddle de-dee!"
And his Aunt Jobiska made him drink,
Lavender water tinged with pink,
For she said, "The World in general knows
There's nothing so good for a Pobble's toes!"

The Pobble who has no toes,
Swam across the Bristol Channel;
But before he set out he wrapped his nose
In a piece of scarlet flannel.
For his Aunt Jobiska said, "No harm
Can come to his toes if his nose is warm;
"And it's perfectly known that a Pobble's toes
Are safe, — provided he minds his nose."

The Pobble swam fast and well
And when boats or ships came near him
He tinkledy-binkledy-winkled a bell
So that all the world could hear him.
And all the Sailors and Admirals cried,
When they saw him nearing the further side, —
"He has gone to fish, for his Aunt Jobiska's
Runcible Cat with crimson whiskers!"

But before he touched the shore,
The shore of the Bristol Channel,
A sea-green Porpoise carried away
His wrapper of scarlet flannel.
And when he came to observe his feet
Formerly garnished with toes so neat
His face at once became forlorn
On perceiving that all his toes were gone!

And nobody ever knew
From that dark day to the present,
Whoso had taken the Pobble's toes,
In a manner so far from pleasant.
Whether the shrimps or crawfish grey,
Or crafty Mermaids stole them away —
Nobody knew; and nobody knows
How the Pobble was robbed of his twice five toes!

The Pobble who has no toes
Was placed in a friendly Bark,
And they rowed him back, and carried him up
To his Aunt Jobiska's Park.
And she made him a feast at his earnest wish
Of eggs and buttercups fried with fish; —
And she said, — "It's a fact the whole world knows,
"That Pobbles are happier without their toes."

Edward Lear

JABBERWOCKY

'Twas brillig, and the slithy toves
Did gyre and gimble in the wabe:
All mimsy were the borogoves,
And the mome raths outgrabe.

"Beware the Jabberwock, my son!
The jaws that bite, the claws that catch!
Beware the Jubjub bird, and shun
The frumious Bandersnatch!"

He took his vorpal sword in hand;
Long time the manxome foe he sought —
So rested he by the Tumtum tree,
And stood awhile in thought.

And, as in uffish thought he stood,
The Jabberwock, with eyes of flame,
Came whiffling through the tulgey wood,
And burbled as it came!

One, two! One, two! And through and through
The vorpal blade went snicker-snack!
He left it dead, and with its head
He went galumphing back.

"And hast thou slain the Jabberwock?
Come to my arms, my beamish boy!
O frabjous day! Callooh, Callay!"
He chortled in his joy.

'Twas brillig, and the slithy toves
Did gyre and gimble in the wabe:
All mimsy were the borogoves,
And the mome raths outgrabe.

Lewis Carroll

THE JUMBLIES

They went to sea in a sieve, they did;
In a sieve they went to sea:
In spite of all their friends could say,
On a winter's morn, on a stormy day,
In a sieve they went to sea.
And when the sieve turned round and round,
And every one cried, "You'll all be drowned!"
They called aloud, "Our sieve ain't big;
But we don't care a button, we don't care a fig:
In a sieve we'll go to sea!"
Far and few, far and few,
Are the lands where the Jumblies live:
Their heads are green, and their hands are blue;
And they went to sea in a sieve.

They sailed away in a sieve, they did,
In a sieve they sailed so fast,
With only a beautiful pea-green veil
Tied with a ribbon, by way of a sail,
To a small tobacco-pipe mast.
And every one said who saw them go,
"Oh! won't they be soon upset, you know?
For the sky is dark, and the voyage is long;
And, happen what may, it's extremely wrong
In a sieve to sail so fast."
Far and few, far and few,
Are the lands where the Jumblies live:
Their heads are green, and their hands are blue;
And they went to sea in a sieve.

The water it soon came in, it did;
The water it soon came in:
So, to keep them dry, they wrapped their feet
In a pinky paper all folded neat;
And they fastened it down with a pin.
And they passed the night in a crockery-jar;
And each of them said, "How wise we are!
Though the sky be dark, and the voyage be long,
Yet we never can think we were rash or wrong,
While round in our sieve we spin."
Far and few, far and few,
Are the lands were the Jumblies live:
Their heads are green, and their hands are blue;
And they went to sea in a sieve.

And all night long they sailed away;
And when the sun went down,
They whistled and warbled a moony song,
To the echoing sound of a coppery gong,
In the shade of the mountains brown.
"O Timballoo! How happy we are
When we live in a sieve and a crockery-jar!
And all night long, in the moonlight pale,
We sail away with a pea-green sail
In the shade of the mountains brown."
Far and few, far and few,
Are the lands where the Jumblies live:
Their heads are green, and their hands are blue;
And they went to sea in a sieve.

They sailed to the Western Sea, they did, —
To a land all covered with trees:
And they bought an owl, and a useful cart,
And a pound of rice, and a cranberry-tart,
And a hive of silvery bees;
And they bought a pig, and some green jackdaws,
And a lovely monkey with lollipop paws,
And forty bottles of ring-bo-ree
And no end of Stilton cheese.
Far and few, far and few,
Are the lands where the Jumblies live:
Their heads are green, and their hands are blue;
And they went to sea in a sieve.

And in twenty years they all came back, —
In twenty years or more;
And every one said, "How tall they've grown!
For they've been to the Lakes, and the Torrible Zone,
And the hills of the Chankly Bore."
And they drank their health, and gave them a feast
Of dumplings made of beautiful yeast;
And everyone said, "If we only live,
We, too, will go to sea in a sieve,
To the hills of the Chankly Bore."
Far and few, far and few,
Are the lands where the Jumblies live:
Their heads are green, and their hands are blue;
And they went to sea in a sieve.

Edward Lear

Things to do

Draw a picture of the Jabberwocky. Remember he's got "jaws that bite", "claws that catch" and "eyes of flame". Use your imagination to picture the rest of him. Draw the background, remembering the jungle-like words that describe it: "All mimsy were the borogoves" and "tulgey wood". You could draw the hero with his "vorpal blade".

HOUSES

I like old houses best, don't you?
They never go cluttering up a view
With roofs too red and paint too new,
With doors too green and blinds too blue!
The old ones look as if they grew,
Their bricks may be dingy, their clapboards askew
From sitting so many seasons through,
But they've learned in a hundred years or two
Not to go cluttering up a view!

Rachel Field

HOUSE COMING DOWN

They're pulling down the house
At the corner of the Square,
The floors and the ceilings
Are out in the air.
The fireplaces so rusty,
The staircases so dusty,
The wallpaper so musty,
Are all laid bare.

It looks like a dollshouse
With the dolls put away,
And the furniture laid by
Against another day;
No bed to lie in,
No pan to fry in,
Or dish to make a pie in,
And nobody to play.

That was the parlour
With the cream-and-yellow scrawls,
That was the bedroom
With the roses on the walls,
There's a dark red lining
In the room they had for dining,
And a brown one, rather shining,
Goes all up the halls.

But where is the lady
In a pretty gown?
Where is the baby
That used to crow and frown?
Oh, the rooms look so little,
The house looks so brittle,
And no one cares a tittle
If it all tumbles down.

Eleanor Farjeon

HOUSE

The ruins of an old house stand
Without a roof, on muddy land,
Each window is a sightless eye
Staring at the city sky.

Locks are broken, every wall
Looks as if about to fall.
The people who lived here, they say,
Just packed up and went away.

And once when I was playing there
Halfway up the curving stair
I thought I heard a laughing sound
Coming from the trampled ground.

Leonard Clark

WANTED

I'm looking for a house
Said the little brown mouse,
                        with
One room for breakfast,
One room for tea,
One room for supper,
And that makes three.

One room to dance in,
When I give a ball,
A kitchen and a bedroom,
Six rooms in all.

Rose Fyleman

Things to do

*Write a poem describing your own house or a house that you
would like to live in. Describe the rooms and what you would
do in them.*

CATS

The black cat yawns,
Opens her jaws,
Stretches her legs,
And shows her claws.

Then she gets up
And stands on four
Long stiff legs
And yawns some more.

She shows her sharp teeth,
She stretches her lip,
Her slice of a tongue
Turns up at the tip.

Lifting herself
On her delicate toes,
She arches her back
As high as it goes.

She lets herself down
With particular care
And pads away,
With her tail in the air.

Mary Britton Miller

CATS

Cats sleep
Anywhere,
Any table,
Any chair,
Top of piano,
Window-ledge,
In the middle,
On the edge,
Open drawer,
Empty shoe,
Anybody's
Lap will do,
Fitted in a
cardboard box,
In the cupboard
With your frocks —
Anywhere!
They don't care!
Cats sleep
Anywhere.

Eleanor Farjeon

TIBS

Tibs is a cat,
Big and furry,
Sometimes scratchy,
Sometimes purry.
Long white whiskers,
Long striped tail,
Don't tread on it
Or Tibs will wail!
Tibs likes fish
From the village shop,
Tibs climbs trees
To the very top.
Tibs likes cream
From the top of the milk,
His fur is soft —
Like warm, striped silk.
Tibs likes to play
With pieces of string,
Tibs runs away
If the doorbell rings.
Tibs likes to sleep
In a sunny place,
And with his little pink tongue
He washes his face.

Daphne Lister

CAT

Cat
purring
four furry paws
walking
delicately
between
flower stems
stalking
butter-
flies.

Keith Bosley

CAT!

Cat!
Scat!
After her, after her,
Sleeky flatterer,
Spitfire chatterer,
Scatter her, scatter her.

Off her mat!
Wuff!
Wuff!
Treat her rough!
Git her, git her,
Whiskery spitter!
Catch her, catch her,
Green-eyed scratcher!

Slathery
Slithery
Misser,
Don't miss her!
Run till you're dithery,

Hithery
Thithery,
Pfitts! Pfitts!
How she spits!
Spitch! Spatch!
Can't she scratch!

Scritching the bark
Of the sycamore tree,
She's reached her ark
And's hissing at me.
Pfitts! Pfitts!
Wuff! Wuff!
Scat
Cat!
That's
That!

Eleanor Farjeon

THE PRIZE

A tiny mouse crept
Out of its hole,
It looked all about,
Then quickly it stole
Across the floor
To the fireside chair,
To look for crumbs
Left lying there.

A shaft of light
Fell across the floor
As silently something
Pushed open the door,
In came a cat,
With green, shiny eyes,
Quickly he pounced
And ran off with his prize!

Joan Sakin

ON A CAT AGEING

He blinks upon the hearth-rug,
And yawns in deep content,
Accepting all the comforts
That Providence has sent.

Louder he purrs and louder
In one glad hymn of praise,
For all the night's adventures,
For quiet restful days.

Life will go on forever,
With all that cat can wish;
Warmth and glad procession
Of fish and milk and fish.

Only — the thought disturbs him —
He's noticed once or twice,
That times are somehow breeding
A nimbler race of mice.

Alexander Gray

MISS TIBBLES

Miss Tibbles is my kitten; white
As day she is and black as night.

She moves in little gusts and breezes
Sharp and sudden as a sneeze is.

At hunting Tibbles has no match.
How I like to see her catch

Moth or beetle, two a penny,
And feast until there isn't any!

Or, if they 'scape her, see her eyes
Grow big as saucers with surprise.

Sometimes I like her calm, unwild,
Gentle as a sleeping child,

And wonder as she lies, a fur ring,
Curled upon my lap, unstirring,
Is it me or Tibbles purring?

Ian Serraillier

A KITTEN

He's nothing much but fur
And two round eyes of blue,
He has a giant purr
And a midget mew.

He darts and pats the air,
He starts and cocks his ear,
When there is nothing there
For him to see and hear.

He runs around in rings,
But why we cannot tell;
With sideways leaps he springs
At things invisible —

Then half-way through a leap
His startled eyeballs close,
And he drops off to sleep
With one paw on his nose.

Eleanor Farjeon

Things to do

*Think of a cat that you know. Think of the way it moves,
washes itself and hunts. Write a poem about the cat,
describing what it looks like, feels like, the sounds it makes
and how it moves. Write the poem so that the reader can
picture the cat. Think of the beautiful description of a cat in
Mary Britton Miller's poem "Cats".*

MACAVITY: THE MYSTERY CAT

Macavity's a Mystery Cat: he's called the Hidden Paw —
For he's the master criminal who can defy the Law.
He's the bafflement of Scotland Yard, the Flying Squad's
    despair:
For when they reach the scene of crime — Macavity's not
    there!

Macavity, Macavity, there's no one like Macavity,
He's broken every human law, he breaks the law of gravity.
His powers of levitation would make a fakir stare,
And when you reach the scene of crime — Macavity's not
    there!
You may seek him in the basement, you may look up in the
    air —
But I tell you once and once again, Macavity's not there!

Macavity's a ginger cat, he's very tall and thin;
You would know him if you saw him, for his eyes are sunken
    in.
His brow is deeply lined with thought, his head is highly
    domed;
His coat is dusty from neglect, his whiskers are uncombed.
He sways his head from side to side, with movements like a
    snake;
And when you think he's half asleep, he's always wide awake.

Macavity, Macavity, there's no one like Macavity,
For he's a fiend in feline shape, a monster of depravity.
You may meet him in a by-street, you may see him in the
    square —
But when a crime's discovered, then Macavity's not there!

He's outwardly respectable. (They say he cheats at cards.)
And his footprints are not found in any file of Scotland
    Yard's.
And when the larder's looted, or the jewel-case is rifled,
Or when the milk is missing, or another Peke's been stifled,
Or the greenhouse glass is broken, and the trellis past
    repair —
Ay, there's the wonder of the thing! Macavity's not there!

And when the Foreign Office find a Treaty's gone astray,
Or the Admiralty lose some plans and drawings by the way
There may be a scrap of paper in the hall or on the stair —
But it's useless to investigate — Macavity's not there!
And when the loss has been disclosed, the Secret Service say:
It must have been Macavity!'' — but he's a mile away.
You'll be sure to find him resting, or a licking of his thumbs,
Or engaged in doing complicated long division sums.

Macavity, Macavity, there's no one like Macavity,
There never was a Cat of such deceitfulness and suavity.
He always has an alibi, and one or two to spare:
At whatever time the deed took place — MACAVITY WASN'T THERE!
And they say that all the Cats whose wicked deeds are widely
   known
(I might mention Mungojerrie, I might mention Griddlebone)
Are nothing more than agents for the Cat who all the time
Just controls their operations: the Napoleon of Crime!

T.S. Eliot

SKIMBLESHANKS: THE RAILWAY CAT

There's a whisper down the line at 11.39
When the Night Mail's ready to depart,
Saying "Skimble where is Skimble has he gone to hunt the
        thimble?
We must find him or the train can't start."
All the guards and all the porters and the stationmaster's
        daughters
They are searching high and low,
Saying "Skimble where is Skimble for unless he's very nimble
Then the Night Mail just can't go."
At 11.42 then the signal's nearly due
And the passengers are frantic to a man —
Then Skimble will appear and he'll saunter to the rear:
He's been busy in the luggage van!
He gives one flash of his glass-green eyes
And the signal goes "All Clear!"
And we're off at last for the northern part
Of the Northern Hemisphere!

You may say that by and large it is Skimble who's in charge
Of the Sleeping Car Express.
From the driver and the guards to the bagmen playing cards
He will supervise them all, more or less.
Down the corridor he paces and examines all the faces
Of the travellers in the First and in the Third;
He establishes control by a regular patrol
And he'd know at once if anything occurred.
He will watch you without winking and he sees what you are
        thinking
And it's certain that he doesn't approve
Of Hilarity and riot, so the folk are very quiet
When Skimble is about and on the move.
You can play no pranks with Skimbleshanks:
He's a Cat that cannot be ignored;
So nothing goes wrong on the Northern Mail
When Skimbleshanks is aboard.

Oh it's very pleasant when you have found your little den
With your name written up on the door.
And the berth is very neat with a newly folded sheet
And there's not a speck of dust on the floor.
There is every sort of light — you can make it dark or bright;
There's a button that you turn to make a breeze.
There's a funny little basin you're supposed to wash your
    face in
And a crank to shut the window if you sneeze.
Then the guard looks in politely and will ask you very
    brightly
'Do you like your morning tea weak or strong?''
But Skimble's just behind him and was ready to remind him,
For Skimble won't let anything go wrong.
And when you creep into your cosy berth
And pull up the counterpane,
You are bound to admit that it's very nice
To know that you won't be bothered by mice —
You can leave all that to the Railway Cat,
The Cat of the Railway Train!

In the middle of the night he is always fresh and bright;
Every now and then he has a cup of tea
With perhaps a drop of Scotch while he's keeping on the
    watch,
Only stopping here and there to catch a flea.
You were fast asleep at Crewe and so you never knew
That he was walking up and down the station;
You were sleeping all the while he was busy at Carlisle,
Where he greets the stationmaster with elation.
But you saw him at Dumfries, where he summons the police
If there's anything they ought to know about:
When you get to Gallowgate there you do not have to wait —
For Skimbleshanks will help you to get out!
He gives you a wave of his long brown tail
Which says: "I'll see you again!
You'll meet without fail on the Midnight Mail
The Cat of the Railway Train''.

T.S. Eliot

GROWLTIGER'S LAST STAND

Growltiger was a Bravo Cat, who travelled on a barge:
In fact he was the roughest cat that ever roamed at large.
From Gravesend up to Oxford he pursued his evil aims,
Rejoicing in his title of "The Terror of The Thames".

His manners and appearance did not calculate to please;
His coat was torn and seedy, he was baggy at the knees;
One ear was somewhat missing, no need to tell you why,
And he scowled upon a hostile world from one forbidding eye.

The cottagers of Rotherhithe knew something of his fame;
At Hammersmith and Putney people shuddered at his name.
They would fortify the hen-house, lock up the silly goose,
When the rumour ran along the shore: GROWLTIGER'S ON THE
    LOOSE!

Woe to the weak canary, that fluttered from its cage;
Woe to the pampered Pekinese, that faced Growltiger's rage;
Woe to the bristly Bandicoot, that lurks on foreign ships,
And woe to any Cat with whom Growltiger came to grips!

But most to Cats of foreign race his hatred had been vowed;
To Cats of foreign name and race no quarter was allowed.
The Persian and the Siamese regarded him with fear —
Because it was a Siamese had mauled his missing ear.

Now on a peaceful summer night, all nature seemed at play,
The tender moon was shining bright, the barge at Molesey lay.
All in the balmy moonlight it lay rocking on the tide —
And Growltiger was disposed to show his sentimental side.

His bucko mate, GRUMBUSKIN, long since had disappeared,
For to the Bell at Hampton he had gone to wet his beard,
And his bosun, TUMBLEBRUTUS, he too had stolen away —
In the yard behind the Lion he was prowling for his prey.

In the forepeak of the vessel Growltiger sate alone,
Concentrating his attention on the Lady GRIDDLEBONE.
And his raffish crew were sleeping in their barrels and
    their bunks —
As the Siamese came creeping in their sampans and their junks.

Growltiger had no eye or ear for aught but Griddlebone,
And the Lady seemed enraptured by his manly baritone,
Disposed to relaxation, and awaiting no surprise —
But the moonlight shone reflected from a hundred bright
    blue eyes.

And closer still and closer the sampans circled round,
And yet from all the enemy there was not heard a sound.
The lovers sang their last duet, in danger of their lives —
For the foe was armed with toasting forks and cruel carving
    knives.

Then Gilbert gave the signal to his fierce Mongolian horde;
With a frightful burst of fireworks the Chinks they swarmed
    aboard.
Abandoning their sampans, and their pullaways and junks,
They battened down the hatches on the crew within their bunks.

Then Griddlebone she gave a screech, for she was badly skeered;
I am sorry to admit it, but she quickly disappeared.
She probably escaped with ease, I'm sure she was not drowned —
But a serried ring of flashing steel Growltiger did surround.

The ruthless foe pressed forward, in stubborn rank on rank;
Growltiger to his vast surprise was forced to walk the plank.
He who a hundred victims had driven to that drop,
At the end of all his crimes was forced to go ker-flip,
    ker-flop.

Oh there was joy in Wapping when the news flew through the
    land;
At Maidenhead and Henley there was dancing on the strand.
Rats were roasted whole at Brentford, and at Victoria Dock,
And a day of celebration was commanded in Bangkok.

T.S. Eliot

Things to do

Make up a cat of your own and write a poem about him. Give him a name and occupation and describe his appearance and personality. Try to make your poem amusing, like T.S. Eliot's poems.

SUNNING

Old Dog lay in the summer sun
Much too lazy to rise and run.
He flapped an ear
At a buzzing fly;
He winked a half-opened
Sleepy eye;
He scratched himself
On an itching spot;
As he dozed on the porch
When the sun was hot.
He whimpered a bit
From force of habit,
While he lazily dreamed
Of chasing a rabbit.
But Old Dog happily lay in the sun,
Much too lazy to rise and run.

James S. Tippett

THE HAIRY DOG

My dog's so furry I've not seen
His face for years and years:
His eyes are buried out of sight,
I only guess his ears.

When people ask me for his breed,
I do not know or care:
He has the beauty of them all
Hidden beneath his hair.

Herbert Asquith

MY PUPPY

It's funny
my puppy
knows just how I feel.

When I'm happy
he's yappy
and squirms like an eel.

When I'm grumpy
he's slumpy
and stays at my heel.

It's funny
my puppy
knows such a great deal.

Aileen Fisher

TOM'S LITTLE DOG

Tom told his dog called Tim to beg,
And up at once he sat,
His two clear amber eyes fixed fast,
His haunches on his mat.

Tom poised a lump of sugar on
His nose; then, "Trust!" says he;
Stiff as a guardsman sat his Tim;
Never a hair stirred he.

"Paid for!" says Tom; and in a trice
Up jerked that moist black nose;
A snap of teeth, a crunch, a munch,
And down the sugar goes!

Walter de la Mare

MY DOG

His nose is short and scrubby;
   His ears hang rather low;
And he always brings the stick back,
   No matter how far you throw.

He gets spanked rather often
   For things he shouldn't do,
Like lying-on-beds, and barking,
   And eating up shoes when they're new.

He always wants to be going
   Where he isn't supposed to go.
He tracks up the house when it's snowing –
   Oh, puppy, I love you so.

Marchette Chute

MY DOG

Have you seen a little dog anywhere about?
A raggy dog, a shaggy dog, who's always looking out
For some fresh mischief which he thinks he really ought to do,
He's very likely, at this minute, biting someone's shoe.

If you see that little dog, his tail up in the air,
A whirly tail, a curly tail, a dog who doesn't care
For any other dog he meets, not even for himself;
Then hide your mats, and put your meat upon the topmost shelf.

If you see a little dog, barking at the cars,
A raggy dog, a shaggy dog, with eyes like twinkling stars,
Just let me know, for though he's bad, as bad as bad can be;
I wouldn't change that dog for all the treasures of the sea.

Emily Lewis

AIREDALE IN GARDEN

fly hum
bee whirr
flower smell
wait
leaf noise
bush moves
beach smell
cat
eyes look
leaf noise
cat moves
bark
path turns
tree shade
bird hops
bee whirr
ear noise
snap
sun burns
flowers bright
tree smell
wait
sun grass
bird flies
ground noise
feet
his feet
gate side
run run
jump
feet stop
clothes smell
ear feel
talk.

Clive Sansom

Things to do

Write a poem about a dog you know. Describe its appearance, behaviour and habits. If it's your dog, write about your relationship with it, how you play with it, take it for walks and look after it.

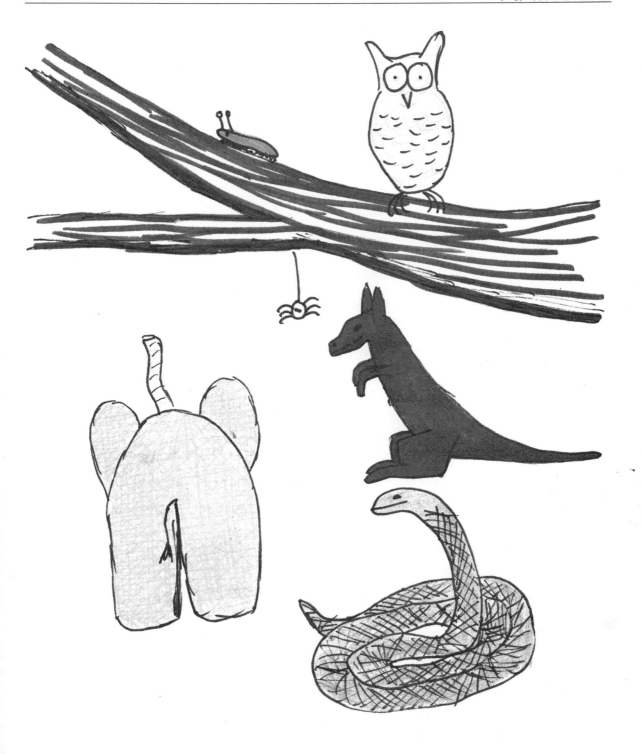

UNDER THE RANGE

Where the gully shadows lie
Deeply blue before the sun,
In the shadow of the range
Wallaby are on the run.

Where the cliffs reach to the sky
In sudden mountains darkly strange,
Where the pine and mallee dare
To climb the jagged range.

He makes his home that none will find,
The wallaby, the secret one,
Alone he runs his soakage pad,
Alone he sits when day is done.

Sits like a statue on the rocks,
His little striped face bright and wise,
And nothing stirs there that is not
Reflected in his eyes.

Is he lonely there at night
When the quiet of night is on?
Does he think the light blown out
If suddenly the stars are gone?

Does he mind the bitter winds
When the evening light has fled?
Does he find a cave of rocks
With a dry earth bed?

Out there the fires of stars are set,
Now frosty winter has begun,
To keep a watch at night for those
Rock wallaby upon the run.

Irene Gough

THE POSSUM TREE

This is the possum's tree,
His claws have left their mark,
Their scrawling tale of visiting,
Sharply in the bark.

He must hunt his berries
In trees that float in mist,
Before the sun has flooded
The hills with amethyst.

He knows a different land,
Where morning wakes too soon
In a secret shadow world
Underneath the moon.

While the wakeful magpie
Plays the lonely flute,
In the silver starlight
He feasts on golden fruit.

None shall know, who come by day,
He haunts the valley floor,
But those who see the name he scratched
Beneath his open door.

Irene Gough

THE LIZARD

There on the sun-hot stone
Why do you wait, alone
And still, so still?
Neck arched, head high, tense and alert, but still,
Still as the stone?

Still is your delicate head,
Like the head of an arrow;
Still is your delicate throat,
Rounded and narrow;
Still is your delicate back,
Patterned in silver and black,
And bright with the burnished sheen that the gum-tips share;

Even your delicate feet
Are still, still as the heat,
With a stillness alive and awake, and intensely aware.
Why do I catch my breath,
Held by your spell?
Listening, waiting — for what?
Will you not tell?
More alive in your quiet than ever the locust can be,
Shrilling his clamorous song from the shimmering tree;
More alive in your motionless grace, as the slow minutes die,
Than the scurrying ants that go hurrying busily by,
I know, if my shadow but fall by your feet on the stone,
In the wink of an eye,
Let me try —
Ah!
He's gone!

Lydia Pender

THE PEOPLE UPSTAIRS

The people upstairs,
The people upstairs
They make such a noise
You would think they were bears.

The way that they gnaw!
The timber they swallow!
It's no wonder that so many
Gum-trees are hollow.

When trees drip with silver,
And thorn scrub lies dim,
When the magpie is singing
The earliest hymn.

At dawn, with the thunder
Of beasts on the hoof,
They gallop for fun
On the galvanized roof.

And although we can send them
No bill for repairs,
We cannot get rid
Of the possums upstairs.

Irene Gough

SNAKE GLIDES

Snake glides
    through grass
        over
           pebbles
              forked tongue
         working
       never
     speaking
        but its
            body
              whispers
                  listen.

Keith Bosley

THE DONKEY

I saw a donkey
One day old,
His head was too big
For his neck to hold;
His legs were shaky
And long and loose,
They rocked and staggered
And weren't much use.

He tried to gambol
And frisk a bit,
But he wasn't quite sure
Of the trick of it.
His queer little coat
Was soft and grey,
And curled at his neck
In a lovely way.

His face was wistful
And left no doubt
That he felt life needed
Some thinking about.
So he blundered round
In venturesome quest,
And then lay flat
On the ground to rest.

Gertrude Hind

MICE

I think mice
Are rather nice.

    Their tails are long,
    Their faces small,
    They haven't any
    Chins at all.
    Their ears are pink,
    Their teeth are white,
    They run about
    The house at night.
    They nibble things
    They shouldn't touch
    And no-one seems
    To like them much.

But I think mice
Are nice.

Rose Fyleman

MOUSE

Little Mouse in grey velvet,
Have you had a cheese-breakfast?
There are no crumbs on your coat,
Did you use a napkin?
I wonder what you had to eat,
And who dresses you in grey velvet?

Hilda Conkling

ANNE AND THE FIELD—MOUSE

We found a mouse in the chalk quarry today
In a circle of stones and empty oil drums
By the fag ends of a fire. There had been
A picnic there; he must have been after the crumbs.

Jane saw him first, a flicker of brown fur
In and out of the charred wood and chalk-white.
I saw him last, but not till we'd turned up
Every stone and surprised him into flight,

Though not far — little zigzag spurts from stone
To stone. Once, as he lurked in his hiding-place,
I saw his beady eyes uplifted to mine.
I'd never seen such terror in so small a face.

I watched, amazed and guilty. Beside us suddenly
A heavy pheasant whirred up from the ground,
Scaring us all; and, before we knew it, the mouse
Had broken cover, skimming away without a sound,

Melting into the nettles. We didn't go
Till I'd chalked in capitals on a rusty can:
THERE'S A MOUSE IN THOSE NETTLES. LEAVE
HIM ALONE. NOVEMBER 15TH. ANNE.

Ian Serraillier

MOUSE

A small mouse
comes every night
to clean my house
by moonlight.

When in my bed
I sleep sound,
like someone dead,
it glides around

the four walls,
the earthen floor.
No crumb falls
unaccounted for.

Starlight or storm,
it matters not:
the dawn's alarm,
the creaking cot

trouble it less
than that I may
rudely miss
supper one day.

My floor is clean,
my table clear:
my mouse has been
gleaning here.

It cannot be
so very fat.
My poverty
must see to that —

but then I know
it cannot be lean:
my house is so
uncommon clean!

Kenneth Mackenzie

MARE

When the mare shows you
her yellow teeth, stuck
with clover and gnawed leaf,
you know they have combed
pastures of spiky grasses,
and tough thickets.

But when you offer her
a sweet, white lump
from the trembling plate
of your palm — she trots
to the gate, sniffs —
and takes it with velvet lips.

Judith Thurman

MAGPIES

Along the road the magpies walk
with hands in pockets, left and right.
They tilt their heads, and stroll and talk.
In their well-fitted black and white

they look like certain gentlemen
who seem most nonchalant and wise
until their meal is served — and then
what clashing beaks, what greedy eyes!

But not one man that I have heard
throws back his head in such a song
of grace and praise — no man nor bird.
Their greed is brief; their joy is long,
For each is born with such a throat
as thanks his God with every note.

Judith Wright

THE EAGLE

He clasps the crag with crooked hands;
Close to the sun in lonely lands,
Ring'd with the azure world, he stands.

The wrinkled sea beneath him crawls;
He watches from his mountain walls,
And like a thunderbolt he falls.

Alfred Lord Tennyson

THE CATERPILLAR

Brown and furry
Caterpillar in a hurry
Take your walk
To the shady leaf, or stalk,
Or what not,
Which may be the chosen spot.
No toad spy you,
Hovering bird of prey pass by you;
Spin and die,
To live again a butterfly.

Christina Rossetti

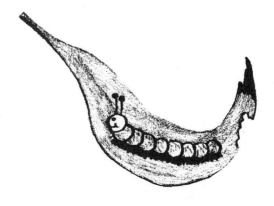

THE TICKLE RHYME

"Who's that tickling my back?" said the wall.
"Me", said a small
 Caterpillar. "I'm learning
 To crawl".

Ian Serraillier

Things to do

1. *Think of your favourite animal. Write a poem describing its characteristics: size, shape, skin, movements, feeding habits and habitat.*

2. *Draw a picture of the animal you have written about.*

THE SHEPHERD

Old Sam Smith
Lived by himself so long,
He thought three people
A "turrible throng".

But he loved "Old Shep",
Who could open and shut
The hide-hinged door
Of his old bark hut;

And he loved the trees,
The sun and the sky,
And the sound of the wind
Though he couldn't tell why.

But besides all these,
He loved, to the full,
The smell of the sheep,
And the greasy wool.

So they buried him out
(For at last he died)
Out, all alone,
On a bleak hill side,
And there's never a sound
But the bleat of the sheep,
As they nibble the mound
That marks his sleep.

Mary Gilmore

ALONE IN THE GRANGE

Strange,
Strange,
Is the little old man
Who lives in the Grange.
Old,
Old;
And they say that he keeps
A box full of gold.
Bowed,
Bowed,
Is his thin little back
That once was so proud.
Soft,
Soft,
Are his steps as he climbs
The stairs to the loft.
Black,
Black,
Is the old shuttered house.
Does he sleep on a sack?

They say he does magic,
That he can cast spells,
That he prowls round the garden
Listening for bells;
That he watches for strangers,
Hates every soul,
And peers with his dark eye
Through the keyhole.

I wonder, I wonder,
As I lie in my bed,
Whether he sleeps with his hat on his head?
Is he really magician
With altar of stone,
Or a lonely old gentleman
Left on his own?

Gregory Harrison

THE BOY FISHING

I am cold and alone,
On my tree-root sitting as still as stone.
The fish come to my net. I scorned the sun,
The voices on the road, and they have gone.
My eyes are buried in the cold pond, under
The cold, spread leaves; my thoughts are silver-wet.
I have ten stickleback, a half-day's plunder,
Safe in my jar. I shall have ten more yet.

E.J. Scovell

THE TUB

My tub is an aquarium
In which the fish is me;
I like to think that I am some
Strange monster of the sea.

Sometimes a mighty whale I am,
The monarch of the deep,
And other times I am a clam
And almost fall asleep.

Then I become a sinking ship
That signals her distress
And tells of a disastrous trip
By yelling "SOS"!

And then I am a lifeboat, manned
By gallant lads and true,
I save myself from drowning and
I get a medal, too!

And then I hear my mother's shout,
That calls me back to shore,
And GEE! I have to clamber out
And be a boy once more!!

George S. Chappell

THE SAILOR

I'd like to be a sailor — a sailor bold and bluff —
Calling out "Ship ahoy!" in manly tones and gruff.
I'd learn to box the compass, and to reef and tack and luff;
I'd sniff and sniff the briny breeze and never get enough.
Perhaps I'd chew tobacco, or an old black pipe I'd puff;
    But I wouldn't be a sailor if . . .
        The sea was very rough.
            Would you?

                C.J. Dennis

THE PORTER

I'd like to be a porter, and always on the run,
Calling out, "Stand aside!" and asking leave of none.
Shoving trucks on people's toes, and having splendid fun;
Slamming all the carriage doors and locking every one —
And, when they asked to be let in, I'd say, "It can't be done."
    But I wouldn't be a porter if . . .
        The luggage weighed a ton.
            Would you?

                C.J. Dennis

THE BARBER

I'd like to be a barber, and learn to shave and clip,
Calling out, "Next please!" and pocketing my tip.
All day you'd hear my scissors going "Snip, Snip, Snip!"
I'd lather people's faces, and their noses I would grip
While I shaved most carefully along the upper lip.
    But I wouldn't be a barber if . . .
        The razor was to slip.
            Would you?

                C.J. Dennis

THE TEACHER

I'd like to be a teacher, and have a clever brain,
Calling out, "Attention, please!" and "Must I speak in
vain?"
I'd be quite strict with boys and girls whose minds I
had to train,
And all the books and maps and things I'd carefully
explain;
I'd make them learn the dates of kings, and all the capes
of Spain;

But I wouldn't be a teacher if . . .
I couldn't use the cane.
Would you?

C.J. Dennis

THE LONELY SCARECROW

My poor old bones — I've only two —
A broomshank and a broken stave,
My ragged gloves are a disgrace,
My one peg-foot is in the grave.

I wear the labourer's old clothes;
Coat, shirt and trousers all undone.
I bear my cross upon a hill
In rain and shine, in snow and sun.

I cannot help the way I look.
My funny hat is full of hay.
— O, wild birds, come and nest in me!
Why do you always fly away?

James Kirkup

SCARECROW INDEPENDENCE

I may look raggy and queer
— but I bow to no man.

My face may look silly and sad
— but I'm no snowman.

I may stand stiff and still
— but hold my head high.

I raise my old top hat to no one
— not even when *you* walk by.

James Kirkup

ONE–EYED JACK

One-eyed Jack, the pirate chief,
Was a terrible, fearsome ocean thief,
He wore a peg
Upon one leg;
He wore a hook —
And a dirty look!
One eyed Jack, the pirate chief —
A terrible, fearsome ocean thief!

Anon.

THE PIRATE DON DURK OF DOWDEE

Ho, for the Pirate Don Durk of Dowdee!
He was as wicked as wicked could be,
But oh, he was perfectly gorgeous to see!
    The pirate Don Durk of Dowdee.

His conscience, of course, was as black as a bat,
But he had a floppety plume on his hat,
And when he went walking it jiggled — like that!
    The Plume of the Pirate Dowdee.

His coat it was crimson and cut with a slash,
And often as ever he twirled his moustache.
Deep down in the ocean the mermaids went splash,
    Because of Don Durk of Dowdee.

Moreover, Dowdee had a purple tattoo,
And stuck in his belt where he buckled it through
Were a dagger, a dirk and a squizzamaroo,
    For fierce was the Pirate Dowdee.

So fearful was he he would shoot at a puff,
And always at sea when the weather grew rough
He drank from a bottle and wrote on his cuff,
    Did Pirate Don Durk of Dowdee.

Oh, he had a cutlass that swung at his thigh,
And he had a parrot called Pepperkin Pye,
And a zigzaggy scar at the end of his eye
    Had Pirate Don Durk of Dowdee.

He kept in a cavern, this buccaneer bold,
A curious chest that was covered with mould,
And all of his pockets were jingly with gold!
    O jing! went the gold of Dowdee.

His conscience, of course, it was crook'd like a squash
But both of his boots made a slickery slash,
And he went through the world with a wonderful swash,
    Did Pirate Don Durk of Dowdee.

It's true he was wicked as wicked could be,
His sins they outnumbered a hundred and three,
But oh, he was perfectly gorgeous to see,
    The Pirate Don Durk of Dowdee.

Mildred Meigs

WHISKERS

He does it every morning, and sometimes twice a day,
I'd rather stand and look at him than go outside and play;
He stands before the mirror and pushes out his chin,
Then he gives a sort of sigh and plugs the razor in.
It's rather like our Hoover, but not as big as that;
And then, of course, it sweeps his face and not the bedroom
                                                        mat.
I know why he does it too; I'll tell you, so you'll know:
Because, each night, while he's in bed, his whiskers start
                                                        to grow;
He has to put a stop to them or else they'd grow all day —
He'd end up with a ten-foot beard then Mum would run away!
Now me, I'd like a ten-foot beard — I've tried to make one
                                                        grow;
I've rubbed my chin with margarine — but did I get one? No!
Mum says she thinks I never will; at least, she hopes I
                                                        won't;
And when I asked her why, she said that little girls just
                                                        don't.
It isn't fair, and anyway, there's something I don't know,
I suppose I could ask Daddy; he might not like it though.
I've wondered and I've wondered, as I've watched him shave
                                                        his chin:
Does it pull his whiskers out? Or does it push them in?

Susan Chafer

89

FATHER SAYS

Father says
Never
let
me
see
you
doing
that
again
father says
tell you once
tell you a thousand times
Come hell or high water
his finger drills my shoulder
never let me see doing that again
My brother knows all his little sayings off by heart
So we practise them in bed at night.

Michael Rosen

Things to do

1. Read C.J. Dennis' poems, "The Sailor", "The Porter", "The Barber" and "The Teacher". Now think of an occupation that would be interesting to write a poem about. Think of the things that you would like about the job and something about the job that you wouldn't like. Try to make your poem amusing.
2. Read the poems "Whiskers" and "Father Says". Now write a poem about your father or another member of your family. Think about their little habits and mannerisms, or something that they especially do.
3. Read the poem "The Pirate Don Durk of Dowdee". Make a note of all the lines in the poem that describe his appearance. Draw a picture of him, showing all those things. Remember he was "perfectly gorgeous to see" and make him like that in your picture.

SEA SHORE

Sandy shore and sea-weed;
Rocks and cockle-shells;
Pebbles round and salty;
Dead fish smells.

Sun on bending water;
Donkeys jingling bells;
Hoofprints in sand-ripples;
Salt-water wells.

Boats against the sunshine;
Seagulls' squealing hells;
Spray on brown faces;
Small boys' yells.

John Kitching

SHORE

Play on the seashore
And gather up shells,
Kneel in the damp sands
Digging wells.

Run on the rocks
Where the seaweed slips,
Watch the waves
And the beautiful ships.

Mary Britton Miller

UPON THE BEACH

Upon the beach
With pail and spade,
My sandy pies and wells I made.

And people passed
On every hand
And left their footprints on the sand.

Then came a wave
With the rushing tide —
And everything was washed aside.

Ilo Orleans

THE POOL IN THE ROCK

In this water, clear as air,
Lurks a lobster in its lair.
Rock-bound weed sways out and in,
Coral-red, and bottle green.
Wondrous pale anemones
Stir like flowers in a breeze.
Fluted scallop, whelk in shell,
And the prowling mackerel.
Winged with snow the sea-mews ride
The brine-keen wind; and far and wide
Sounds on the hollow thunder of the tide.

Walter de la Mare

THE SEA SHELL

Sea Shell, Sea Shell,
Sing me a song, O please!
A song of ships and sailor men,
Of parrots and tropical trees;
Of islands lost in the Spanish Main
Which no man ever may see again;
Of fishes and corals under the waves,
And sea horses' stables in great green caves.
Sea Shell, Sea Shell,
Sing me a song, O please!

Amy Lowell

WAVES

There are big waves and little waves,
Green waves and blue,
Waves you can jump over,
Waves you can dive through,
Waves that rise up
Like a great water wall,
Waves that swell softly
And don't break at all.
Waves that can whisper,
Waves that can roar,
And tiny waves that run at you
Running on the shore.

Eleanor Farjeon

HOLIDAYS

Silvery sea
Sugary sand
Scallopy seaweed
Cliffs, rocky land:
Ships a-sailing
Gathering shells
Watching waves
Recede and swell:
Sand in toes
Wind in the hair
Racing along
Sand firm and bare:
Sunshine days
Holiday fun
Isn't it lovely?
They've just begun.

Frances Allen

Things to do

*Write a poem about when you go to the beach. Describe the
sea and the sand. Describe your feelings as you play in the
sand, what the sand feels like and what you can do with it.
Describe the feel of the water. Is it cold? Is it rough or calm?
Describe the things that you find at the beach, such as shells,
crabs and seaweed.*

THE BROKEN TOYS

In the broken box
The broken toys —
    Dusty,
Battered and rusty,
Tattered and torn,
    Forlorn, forlorn.

The snapped strings
And the busted springs,
The rag-doll raggy and rent,
The pink tin teaset buckled and bent,
    The crashed plane,
    The car, the train —
Smashed in a terrible accident.

And all the dolls' eyes
Rolling loose like heavy marbles
Up the doll's house stairs and down
The stairs of the overturned house . . . .
The dead wheels of a clockwork mouse.

In the broken box
The broken toys —
    Dusty,
Battered and rusty,
Tattered and torn,
    Forlorn, forlorn.

James Kirkup

THE BALLOON MAN

He always comes on market days,
And holds balloons — a lovely bunch —
And in the market square he stays,
And never seems to think of lunch.

They're red and purple, blue and green,
And when it is a sunny day
Thou' carts and people get between
You see them shining far away.

And some are big and some are small,
All tied together with a string,
And if there is a wind at all,
They tug and tug like anything.

Some day perhaps he'll let them go
And we shall see them sailing high,
And stand and watch them from below —
They would look pretty in the sky!

Rose Fyleman

BALLOONS

Balloons mean happiness and fun
And pleasant things to do;
Balloons mean parties, street parades,
And visits to the zoo.

They can be long, like sausages,
Or all round, like a ball,
They can be fat, or thin, or curved,
Or any shape at all.

They feel so light, and soft, and smooth;
They always make me glad.
No one who's holding a balloon
Could possibly feel sad.

Eva May

MY BALL

Why does my ball
So often fall
Where a ball isn't meant to be at all?
It lands on the roof, or gets caught in a tree;
It knocks over tables, and full cups of tea;
It drops among chairs where people are sitting,
And always straight on to somebody's knitting;
It sails over fences and tears down a vine,
Or leaves mud on sheets hanging up on a line,
Or else it hits Mr. Stewart's best plums,
Or Mrs. Jones' prize chrysanthemums.
Oh, why does my ball
So often fall
Where a ball isn't meant to be at all?

                                        Eva May

MY KITE

My kite must see a lot of things
As it glides through the air —
It flies so high above the ground,
It can look anywhere.
It meets the birds, the clouds, the sun —
It's happy and it's free!
You'd think that it could tell the most
Exciting tales to me.
But when I ask: "Where have you been —
Please, won't you tell me what you've seen?"
Do you know what I've heard?
Not a word!

                                        Eva May

THE KITE

How bright on the blue
Is a kite when it's new!

With a dive and a dip
It snaps its tail

Then soars like a ship
With only a sail

As over tides
Of wind it rides,

    Climbs to the crest
    Of a gust and pulls,

    Then seems to rest
    As wind falls.

    When string goes slack
    You wind it back

    And run until
    A new breeze blows.

        And its wings fill
        And up it goes!

        How bright on the blue
        Is a kite when it's new!

        But a raggeder thing
        You never will see

        When it flaps on a string
        In the top of a tree.

Harry Behn

THE BALLOON SELLER

I'd like to peddle toy balloons;
With globes like jolly suns and moons
Bobbing and bouncing there, I'd stay
Holding them high the live-long day.

I'd make them dance like anything,
All fastened to a bit of string,
Their golds and greens, and blues and reds
Glimmering over people's heads.

And all the folks would turn and stare,
And long to free them on the air.

Elizabeth Fleming

RIDING ON MY BIKE

Riding on my bike —
That is what I like!
Like the wind
So fast I go,
Past the houses
in a row.
Now fast and faster,
Set the brake!
Down hill I go,
What speed I make!
Then up the hill
Without a stop,
I push and pedal
To the top.
I pedal hard,
I pedal fast;
Back home again
I come at last.

Lois Lenski

MY DOLL'S PRAM

How proud I am
When I push my pram
With my doll and my teddy inside!
They look so snug
Underneath their rug
As they lie there, side by side.
And sometimes, when they're fast asleep,
Someone will ask me: "May I peep
Into your pram for just a minute?
What lovely children you have in it!"

Eva May

Things to do

*Think of your favourite toy and write a poem about it.
Describe its appearance, how you play with it and
why you like it.*

COLOUR

I see different colours
Everywhere around,
Sky and trees and buildings,
Flowers on the ground;
Motor cars and buses,
Clothes and shoes and hats,
Different coloured animals —
Horses, dogs and cats;
Sailing ships and water,
Letter boxes too,
Red and pink and purple,
Yellow, green and blue —
And so many others
I could never say,
Colour all around me,
Somewhere every day.

Joan Mellings

WHAT IS BLUE?

Blue is a lake,
A sapphire ring.
You can smell blue
In many a thing:
Lupins and larkspur,
Forget-me-nots too.
And if you listen
You can hear blue
In wind over water
And wherever flax blooms
And when evening steps into
Lonely rooms.

Mary O'Neill

WHAT IS PINK?

What is pink? a rose is pink
By the fountain's brink.
What is red? a poppy's red
In its barley bed.
What is blue? The sky is blue
Where the clouds float thro'
What is white? a swan is white
Sailing in the light.
What is yellow? pears are yellow,
Rich and ripe and mellow.
What is green? the grass is green,
With small flowers between.
What is violet? clouds are violet
In the summer twilight.
What is orange? why, an orange,
Just an orange!

Christina Rossetti

WHAT IS RED?

Red is a sunset
Blazing and bright.
Red is feeling brave
With all your might.
Red is a sunburn
Spot on your nose.
Sometimes red
Is a red red rose.
Red squiggles out
When you cut your hand.
Red is a brick
And the sound of a band.
Red is hotness
You get inside
When you're embarrassed
And want to hide.
Fire-cracker, fire-engine
Fire-flicker red —
And when you're angry
Red runs through your head.
Red is an Indian,
A Valentine heart,
The trimmings on
A circus cart.
Red is a lipstick
Red is a shout
Red is a signal
That says: "Watch out!"
Red is a great big
Rubber ball.
Red is the giantest
Colour of all.
Red is a show-off,
No doubt about it —
But can you imagine
Living without it?

Mary O'Neill

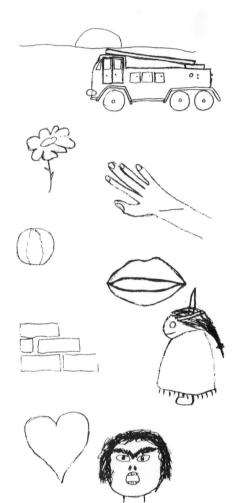

Things to do

Think of your favourite colour and think of all the things that are that colour. Write a poem about that colour. Mention the things that are that colour but also try and describe the effect that colour has on your senses.

A WINDY DAY

This wind brings all dead things to life,
Branches that lash the air like whips
And dead leaves rolling in a hurry
Or peering in a rabbit's bury

Or trying to push down a tree;
Gates that fly open to the wind
And close again behind,
And fields that are a flowing sea
And make the cattle look like ships;

Straws glistening and stiff
Lying on air as on a shelf
And pond that leaps to leave itself;
And feathers too that rise and float,
Each feather changed into a bird,
And line-hung sheets that crack and strain;

Even the sun-greened coat,
That through so many winds has served,
The scarecrow struggles to put on again.

Andrew Young

HAPPY WIND

Oh, happy wind, how sweet
Thy life must be!
The great, proud fields of gold
Run after thee:
And here are flowers, with heads
To nod and shake;
And dreaming butterflies
To tease and wake.
Oh, happy wind, I say,
To be alive this day.

Anon.

THE WIND

The wind is angry:
Hear him roar,
Rattle and pull
And bang the door.

The wind is sad
It seems to me:
I hear him sighing
In the tree.

The wind is happy,
Full of fun:
He's snatched my hat —
Away I run
    and run
      and run
        and run
          and run —
            and catch it.

Anne Dreyer

A WINDY DAY

Blow, wind, blow!
Blow me down the street;
Blow me round the corner,
Blow me off my feet!

Whirl me past the houses,
Dance me through the town,
Chase me up the hillside,
Race me going down.

Blow, wind, blow!
Blow me up the lane,
Faster, faster blow me now,
And blow me home again!

Margaret Janidin

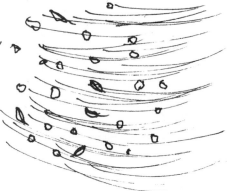

WINDY NIGHTS

Rumbling in the chimneys,
   Rattling at the doors,
Round the roofs and round the roads
   The rude wind roars;
Raging through the darkness,
   Raving through the trees,
Racing off again across
   The great grey seas.

Rodney Bennett

THE WIND

I can get through a doorway without any key,
And strip the leaves from the great oak tree.

I can drive storm-clouds and shake tall towers,
Or steal through a garden and not wake the flowers.

Seas I can move and ships I can sink;
I can carry a house-top or the scent of a pink.

When I am angry I can rave and riot;
And when I am spent, I lie quiet as quiet.

James Reeves

A SONG OF WIND

Hark to the song of the scattering, scurrying,
Blustering, bullying, bellowing, hurrying wind!
Over the hills it comes, laughing and rollicking,
Curling and whirling, flying and frolicking,
    Spinning the clouds that are scattered and thinned,
       And shouting a song
       As it gallops along —
    A song that is nothing but wind.

This is the song of the galloping, hurrying.
Gusty, and dusty, and whirling, and worrying wind.
Over the hill it comes laughing and rollicking,
Yelling, and swooping, and flying, and frolicking,
    Shaking the fences so solidly pinned,
       And shrieking a song
       As it gallops along —
    A terrible song that is wind.

Will Lawson

WHAT THE WIND DOES

It taunts and teases the leaves on a tree,
It tosses and topples a small ship at sea,
It whistles and whispers and blusters and roars —
And blows into houses through windows and doors.

The wind can be kind, a gentle caress,
The wind can be cruel, bringing distress;
It can blow cool in the heat of the day,
Or blow icy cold, driving summer away.

It plays with the clouds, it wanders at night,
The wind is a friend when you're flying a kite,
Sometimes it's happy, sometimes it's vexed —
Nobody knows what the wind will do next.

Joan Mellings

Things to do

Write a poem about the wind. As these poets have described, the wind can be very strong and powerful and do a lot of damage or it can be a very welcome breeze on a hot day. Write about some of the things the wind can do. Write what it feels like to be out on a windy day. Does it make you want to run about and shout?

RAINY DAY

I love to watch the drops of rain
That tumble down the window-pane.
When first the rain begins to fall
They hardly seem to move at all.
But when it starts to pour outside,
Then down the window-pane they slide.
I watch them gather on the ledge
Until they spill over the edge,
And make a puddle down below.
I see it grow . . . and grow . . . and grow . . .
Then when the shower of rain has passed,
And I'm allowed outside at last,
In big strong boots I go to see
The paddling place that's all for me!

Ivy Russell

RAINY NIGHT

I like the town on rainy nights
  When everything is wet —
When all the town has magic lights
  And streets of shining jet!

When all the rain about the town
  Is like a looking-glass —
And all the lights are upside down
  Below me as I pass. . . .

Irene Thompson

RAIN

From under the roof of my umbrella
I saw the washed pavement lapping
  beneath my feet, the newsposters
    lying smeared with dirt at the
      crossings, the tracks of the buses
        in the liquid mud. . . .

Logan Pearsall Smith

RAIN

Rain and rain is all I see
Falling on roof and stone and tree,
And all I hear is rain and rain
Hush-hushing on lawn and lane.

Moor and meadow, fern and flower
Drink the raindrops, hour by hour.
Now sparkling are the ivy leaves
That catch the drops from farmhouse eaves!

When in my attic bed I lie
I hear it fall from the cloudy sky,
Hush-hushing all around
With its low and lulling sound.

James Reeves

RAIN

It's good to lie in bed at night
And hear the sweeping rain
Go patter patter on the roof
And knock against the pane

It croaks and gurgles down the spout,
And swishes through the leaves,
And makes the curly creeper drip
That twines about the eaves.

All snug and warm in blankets soft
I hear a windy song
Like curlews in the lonely bush
That wail the whole night long.

L.H. Allen

CITY RAIN

Rain in the city!
  I love to see it fall
Slantwise where the buildings crowd
  Red brick and all.
Streets of shiny wetness
  Where the taxis go,
With people and umbrellas all
  Bobbing to and fro.

Rain in the city!
  I love to hear it drip
When I am cosy in my room
  Snug as any ship,
With toys spread on the table,
  With a picture book or two,
And the rain like a rumbling tune that sings
  Through everything I do.

Rachel Field

BLOSSOM TIME

"This rain should bring the mushrooms up
  And make the flowers grow.'"
So said my father. Sure enough,
There soon began to show
In paddocks bare the buttons round
Of mushrooms, white as snow.

The flowers, of course, took weeks and weeks
To reach their full display,
For seed and root and leaf and bud
Had each a part to play;
And it was worth the waiting time
To see their blossoms gay.

But on the very day it rained,
As down the first drops sped,
There grew and blossomed instantly
A street of blue, green, red —
Where, opening over hurrying folk,
Umbrella petals spread!

Thea Shipley

RAIN

The lights are all on, though its just past mid-day,
There are no more indoor games we can play,
No one can think of anything to say,
It rained all yesterday, it's raining today,
It's grey outside, inside me it's grey.

I stare out of the window, fist under my chin,
The gutter leaks drips on the lid of the dustbin,
When they say "Cheer up", I manage a grin,
I draw a fish on the glass with a sail-sized fin,
It's sodden outside, and it's damp within.

Matches, bubbles and paper pour into the drains,
Clouds smother the sad laments from the trains,
Grandad says it brings on his rheumatic pains,
The moisture's got right inside of my brains,
It's raining outside, inside me it rains.

Brian Lee

RAIN

Raindrops on my window,
Dark clouds in the sky,
In the street below me,
Cars go splashing by.

Here comes Father hurrying,
His umbrella held up high,
His shoes are wet; his coat is wet,
He heaves a weary sigh.

The fire is lit; the room is warm;
He'll soon be dry again,
While cars and people hurry on,
Still soaking wet with rain.

Joan Sakin

GET WET? WHO? ME?

When I go walking in the rain
I wear a plastic coat,
And gum boots that go slosh, slosh, slosh
Through puddles on the road.

I take my red umbrella, or
Put on a plastic hat;
How could I possibly get wet
When I'm dressed like that?

Eva May

Things to do

1. How do you feel when it rains? Do you like going out in
   the rain or do you prefer to stay indoors? Does the rain
   make you feel depressed? Write a poem about your
   feelings when it rains.

2. Write a poem describing the scene on a rainy day.
   Describe the people wearing raincoats, wellingtons and
   umbrellas. Describe the cars with their headlights and
   windscreen wipers going. Describe the roads and
   pavements shining wet with puddles.

STOPPING BY WOODS ON A SNOWY EVENING

Whose woods these are I think I know.
His house is in the village though;
He will not see me stopping here
To watch his woods fill up with snow.

My little horse must think it queer
To stop without a farmhouse near
Between the woods and frozen lake
The darkest evening of the year.

He gives his harness bell a shake
To ask if there is some mistake.
The only other sound's the sweep
Of easy wind and downy flake.

The woods are lovely, dark and deep.
But I have promises to keep,
And miles to go before I sleep,
And miles to go before I sleep.

Robert Frost

SNOW TOWARD EVENING

Suddenly the sky turned gray,
The day,
Which had been bitter and chill,
Grew soft and still.
Quietly
From some invisible blossoming tree
Millions of petals cool and white
Drifted and blew,
Lifted and flew,
Fell with the falling night.

Melville Cane

SNOWFLAKES

Soft white feathery snowflakes
Covered the garden today.
Covered the birdbath, the gate and the wall,
Over them spread a frosty white shawl,
And hid all the dens where I play.

Soft white feathery snowflakes
Lie deep on my window sill.
They can't cover me for I'm snug in my bed,
I've pulled my blue eiderdown over my head,
And I lie very warm and still.

Grace Hamblin

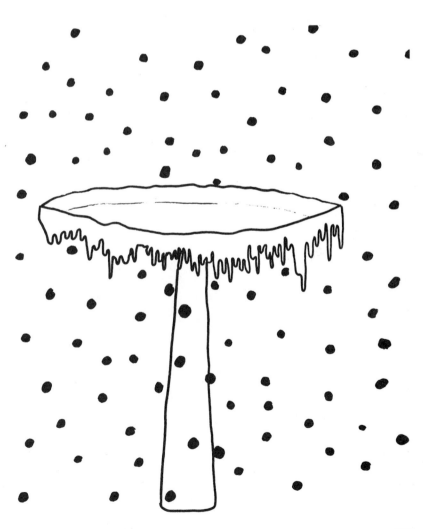

SNOWFLAKES

Snowflakes, snowflakes, twirling down,
Covering the fields and town
Past the trees and window light,
With a magic coat of white.

Snowflakes, snowflakes, soft and deep,
While I'm lying fast asleep,
Dreaming of your welcome fall,
On the roof and chimneys tall.

Snowflakes, snowflakes, bringing joy,
To every happy girl and boy.
Sudden snowballs from the hedges,
Flying down the slopes on sledges.

Snowflakes, snowflakes, when you pass
From the garden and the grass,
Best of all the gifts you bring,
Snowdrops — promise of the Spring.

Edgar W. Goodall

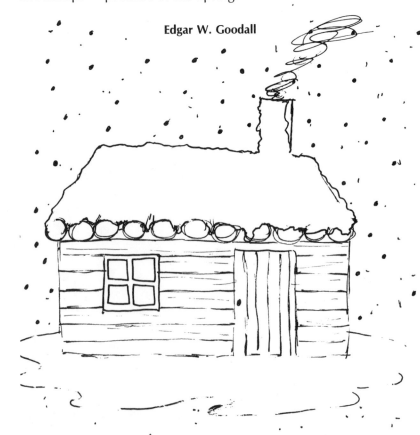

THE SNOWFLAKE

Before I melt,
Come, look at me!
This lovely icy filigree!
Of a great forest
In one night
I make a wilderness
of white:
By skyey cold
Of crystals made,
All softly, on
Your finger laid,
I pause, that you
My beauty see:
Breathe, and I vanish
Instantly.

Walter de la Mare

SNOW

The snow fell softly all the night.
It made a blanket soft and white.
It covered houses, flowers and ground,
But did not make a single sound!

Alice Wilkins

DEATH OF A SNOWMAN

I was awake all night,
Big as a polar bear,
Strong and firm and white.
The tall black hat I wear
Was draped with ermine fur.
I felt so fit and well
Till the world began to stir
And the morning sun swell.
I was tired, began to yawn;
At noon in the humming sun
I caught a severe warm;
My nose began to run.
My hat grew black and fell,
Was followed by my grey head.
There was no funeral bell,
But by tea-time I was dead.

Vernon Scannell

Questions

1. *In all these poems the poets create an atmosphere of
    quiet and stillness as the snow falls and covers everything.
    What language is used to describe the snow and to create
    this atmosphere?*

2. *What happened to the snowman in "Death of a
    Snowman"?*

DAFFODILS

I made a little garden bed
Beneath the apple tree.
I waited for the autumn
When the leaves were falling free.
Then I planted daffodils,
The bulbs were brown and dry —
I didn't really think they'd grow
But I thought I'd have a try.
Now that Spring is here at last,
Gone is the Winter cold.
The bed beneath the apple tree
Is a mass of shiny gold.

Mary Mathias

FROM OLD AUSTRALIAN WAYS

The wind is in the barley-grass,
    The wattles are in bloom;
The breezes greet us as they pass
    With honey-sweet perfume;
The parakeets go screaming by
    With flash of golden wing,
And from the swamp the wild-ducks cry
    Their long-drawn note of revelry,
Rejoicing at the spring.

A.B. Paterson

SPRING

The last snow is going,
Brooks are overflowing,
And a sunny wind is blowing
    Swiftly along.

Through the sky birds are blowing,
On earth green is showing,
You can feel earth growing
    So quiet and strong.

A sunny wind is blowing,
Farmer's busy sowing,
Apple trees are snowing,
And shadows grow long.

Now the wind is slowing,
Cows begin lowing,
Evening clouds are glowing
And dusk is full of song.

Harry Behn

SPRING

Now the sleeping creatures waken —
    Waken, waken;
Blossoms with soft winds are shaken —
    Shaken, shaken;
Squirrels scamper and the hare
Runs races which the children share
Till their shouting fills the air.

Now the woodland birds are singing —
    Singing, singing;
Over field and orchard winging —
    Winging, winging;
Swift and swallow unaware
Weave such beauty on the air
That the children hush and stare.

Raymond Wilson

Things to do

1. *What happens in the spring? What happens to all
    the birds, animals, trees and plants? Why does
    everyone feel happy in the spring?*

2. *Write a poem describing all the new
    life and the feeling of joy that everyone gets
    in the spring.*

SUMMER AFTERNOON

Where shall we go?
    What shall we play?
What shall we do
    On a hot summer day?

We'll sit in the swing,
    Go low, Go high,
And drink lemonade
    Till the glass is dry.

One straw for you,
    One straw for me,
In the cool green shade
    Of the walnut tree.

Marion Edey & Dorothy Grider

A DRAGON FLY

When the heat of the summer
Made drowsy the land
A dragonfly came
And sat on my hand.

With its blue-jointed body,
And wings like spun glass,
It lit on my fingers
As though they were grass.

Eleanor Farjeon

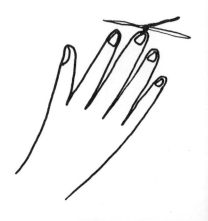

HOT DAY

It was too hot to play,
    So I lay down.
I listened to the crickets,
    Lazing on a stone,
Singing drowsily as they dozed.

The lizard lay basking
    Motionless, without a wink
Of an eye;
    His skin shining
Like a diamond.

Slowly the cows moved
    As they grazed;
A sudden breeze
    Rippled the grass.

The daisy's eye
    Stared up,
To where its golden eye
    Met the golden eye
Of the sun.

Anon.

A HOT DAY

Cotton-wool clouds loiter.
A lawn mower very far
Birrs. Then a bee comes
To a crimson rose and softly,
Deftly and fatly crams
A velvet body in.

A.S.J. Tessimond

Things to do

Three of these poems on summer describe insects. Write a poem on summer describing the sound of insects, the heat, the feeling of drowsiness, the sounds of children playing or people mowing their lawns. Try to conjure up the atmosphere of summer in your poem.

THE LEAVES

The leaves had a wonderful frolic,
   They danced to the wind's loud song,
They whirled, and they floated, and scampered,
   They circled and flew along.

The moon saw the little leaves dancing,
   Each looked like a small brown bird.
The man in the moon smiled and listened,
   And this is the song he heard.

The north wind is calling, is calling,
   And we must whirl round and round.
And then when our dancing is ended
   We'll make a warm quilt for the ground.

Anon.

AUTUMN WOODS

I like the woods in Autumn
When dry leaves hide the ground,
When the trees are bare
And the wind sweeps by
With a lonesome rushing sound.

I can rustle the leaves in Autumn
And I can make a bed
In the thick dry leaves
That have fallen
From the bare trees
Overhead.

James S. Tippett

AUTUMN

Tiny little parachutes
Dropping through the air —
Fluffy seeds of thistledown
Are flying everywhere.

Lots of little aeroplanes
Spinning down the sky —
Brownish seeds of sycamore
Are whirling, whirling by.

The air is full of Autumn things —
Leaves of red and brown,
Acorns, berries, nuts and seeds,
All tumbling, tumbling down.

Anon.

WHEN MARY GOES WALKING

When Mary goes walking
The Autumn winds blow
The Poplars they curtsey,
The Larches bend low,
The Oaks and the Beeches
Their gold they fling down.
To make her a carpet,
To make her a crown!

Anon.

AUTUMN SCENE

It's quiet in the forest
Dark and cool.
The trees peep over
Towards the pool.
Leaves fall softly,
Float like boats,
Hazel nuts blush
In their Autumn coats.
Above the pine hops
A pigeon calls,
Softly, softly,
The sound falls.

Barbara Edmonds

AUTUMN LEAVES

Autumn leaves
Come floating down,
Red and yellow,
Green and brown.

Twisting, tumbling
To the ground,
Twirling, swirling,
Round and round.

Merril Brown

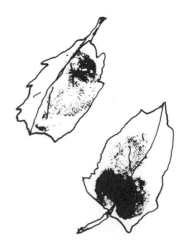

Things to do

Write a poem describing the trees in autumn. Describe the leaves changing colour and falling from the trees. Describe the feeling and sound of walking through the leaves on the ground. Describe the atmosphere, sights and smells of an autumn day.

WINTER FIRE

Crackle, crackle,
Burn and glow,
Watch the fire
Start to grow.

Higher, higher,
Leap and spread,
Darting tongues —
Gold and red.

Quicker, slower,
Rise and fall,
Shadows dancing
On the wall.

Smaller, smaller,
Sink and die,
As the night hours
Swiftly fly.

Nestle, nestle,
In your bed,
Winking coals,
Glowing red.

Joan Mellings

FOG

Slowly the fog,
Hunch-shouldered with a gray face,
Arms wide, advances,
Finger-tips touching the way
Past the dark houses
And dark gardens of roses.
Up the short street from the harbour,
Slowly the fog,
Seeking, seeking;
Arms wide, shoulders hunched,
Searching, searching.
Out through the streets to the fields,
Slowly the fog —
A blind man hunting the moon.

F.R. McCreary

FOG

The fog comes
on little cat feet.

It sits looking
over harbour and city
on silent haunches
and then moves on.

Carl Sandburg

JACK FROST

Look out! Look out!
Jack Frost is about!
He's after our fingers and toes;
And, all through the night,
The gay little sprite
Is working where nobody knows.

He'll climb each tree,
So nimble is he,
His silvery powder he'll shake;
To windows he'll creep,
And while we're asleep,
Such wonderful pictures he'll make.

Across the grass,
He'll merrily pass
And change all its greenness to white:
Then home he will go
And laugh, "Ho! Ho! Ho!
What fun I have had in the night".

Cecily E. Pike

NIGHT FROST

Walking through the wood at day,
All the trees were dark and grey,
Something happened in the night —
All the world is shining white.

Jack Frost's magic brush has been
Painting silver on the scene.
Every leaf on every bough
Sparkles crystal pendants now.

From the line of every hedge
Boldly gleams a fiery edge.
Jewelled twigs beneath me crack
As I tread the woodland track.

Edgar W. Goodall

Things to do

1. *What is your favourite thing about winter: playing in the snow, seeing all the patterns the frost has made, getting all wrapped up to go out into the cold or sitting by a nice warm fire?*

2. *Write a poem about the things you like or do not like about winter.*

FULL MOON

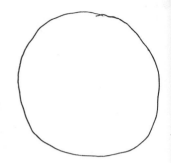

One night as Dick lay fast asleep,
　　Into his drowsy eyes
A great still light began to creep
　　From out the silent skies.
It was the lovely moon's, for when
　　He raised his dreamy head,
Her surge of silver filled the pane
　　And streamed across his bed.
So, for awhile, each gazed at each —
　　Dick and the solemn moon —
Till, climbing slowly on her way,
　　She vanished, and was gone.

Walter de la Mare

THE WHITE WINDOW

The Moon comes every night to peep
　　Through the window where I lie,
And I pretend to be asleep;
　　But I watch the Moon as it goes by,
And it never makes a sound.

It stands and stares, and then it goes
　　To the house that's next to me,
Stealing on its tippy-toes,
　　To peep at folk asleep maybe;
And it never makes a sound.

James Stephens

SILVER

Slowly, silently, now the moon
Walks the night in her silver shoon;
This way, and that, she peers, and sees
Silver fruit upon silver trees;
One by one the casements catch
Her beams beneath the silvery thatch;
Couched in his kennel, like a log,
With paws of silver sleeps the dog;
From their shadowing cote the white breasts peep
Of doves in a silver-feathered sleep;
A harvest mouse goes scampering by,
With silver claws, and silver eye;
And moveless fish in the water gleam,
By silver reeds in a silver stream.

Walter de la Mare

FLYING

I saw the moon
One windy night,
Flying so fast —
All silvery white —
Over the sky,
Like a toy balloon
Loose from its string —
A runaway moon.
The frosty stars
Went racing past,
Chasing her on
Ever so fast.
Then everyone said,
"It's the clouds that fly,
And the stars and moon
Stand still in the sky."
But I don't mind —
I saw the moon
Sailing away
Like a toy
Balloon.

J.M. Westrup

THE NIGHT WILL NEVER STAY

The night will never stay,
The night will still go by,
Though with a million stars
You pin in to the sky;
Though you bind it with the blowing wind
And buckle it with the moon,
The night will slip away
Like sorrow or a tune.

Eleanor Farjeon

Questions
The four poems about the moon all give the moon a
personality. What do they describe the moon as doing?

INDEX OF TITLES

INDEX OF AUTHORS

INDEX OF FIRST LINES